Disney

Henry HuggleMonster

Written by Sheila Sweeny Higginson

Illustrated by Premise Entertainment

bendon®

It's Roaring Racer Day for the Monster Scouts!

Henry wants to get a racing patch.

"Time to pack up and move out, Monster Scouts!"
says Daddo.

Find the belt that matches Henry's Monster Scout belt.

The Monster Scouts are **ROAR**-tastic!

"Roberto's roar sounds a lot like my roar," says Henry.

Assistant Scout Master Eduardo
brings the racer supplies.

Henry wants a steering wheel that is shaped like a triangle. Can you find it?

"A triangle! That's perfect!" shouts Roberto.

"Come and get your paint," calls Daddo.
"We've even got green-urple!"

Henry chooses red.

Unscramble the color names.

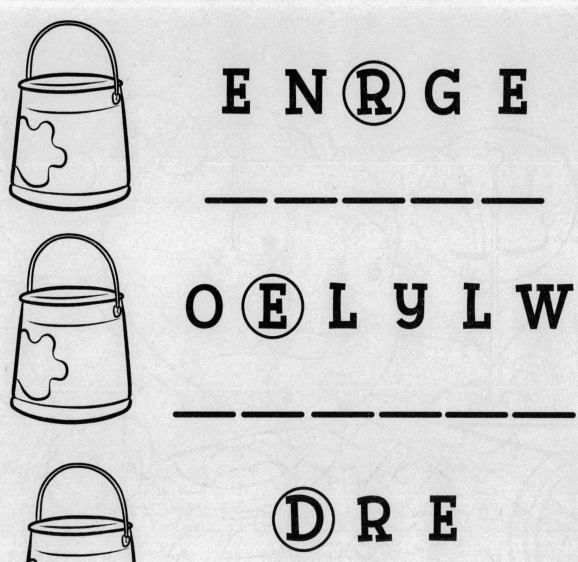

E N Ⓡ G E

_ _ _ _ _

O Ⓔ L Y L W

_ _ _ _ _ _

Ⓓ R E

_ _ _

Copy the letters in the circles to see what color
Roberto painted his car.

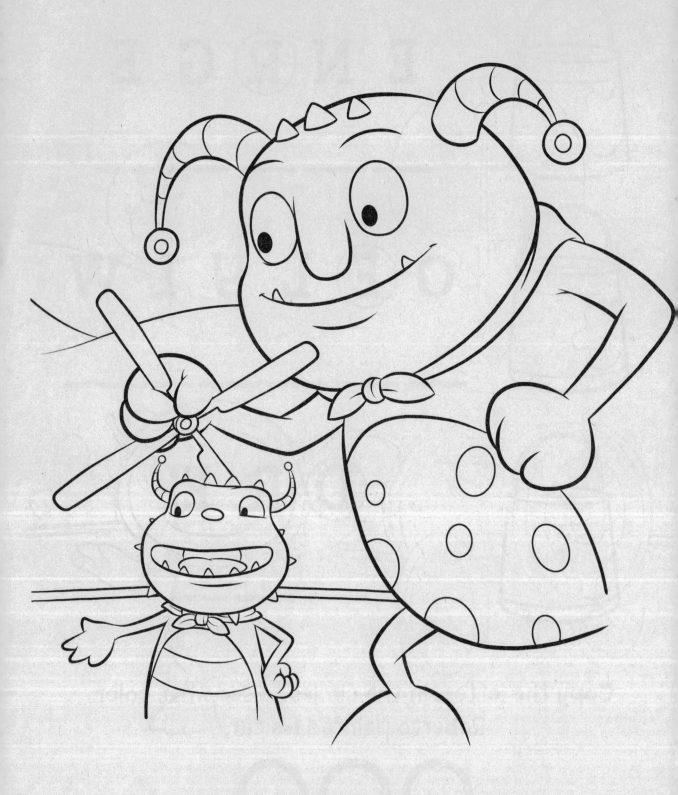

"Now, scouts, it's time to unveil your roaring racers!"
says Daddo.

"I call mine **Rolling Thunder!**" says Denzel. ©Disney

"I call mine **The Zoomster!**" announces
Cobby.

"I call mine—**Red Lightning!**" Roberto says.

What would your roaring racer look like?

"He copied me!" Henry protests. "Look!"

Henry needs a Huggle-break!

How many trees did Henry fly over?
Write your answer below.

Answer

"This just isn't right," says Henry. "I've got to go talk to Roberto."

"You copied me!" says Henry.

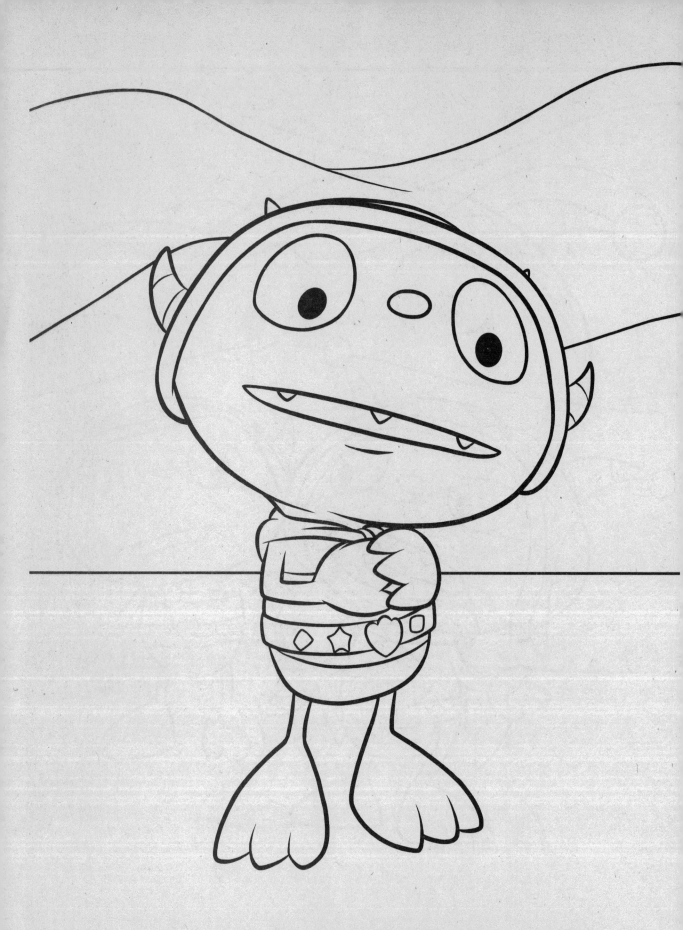

"I'm sorry, Henry," says Roberto. "I didn't mean to make you mad. Your racer is just so cool!"

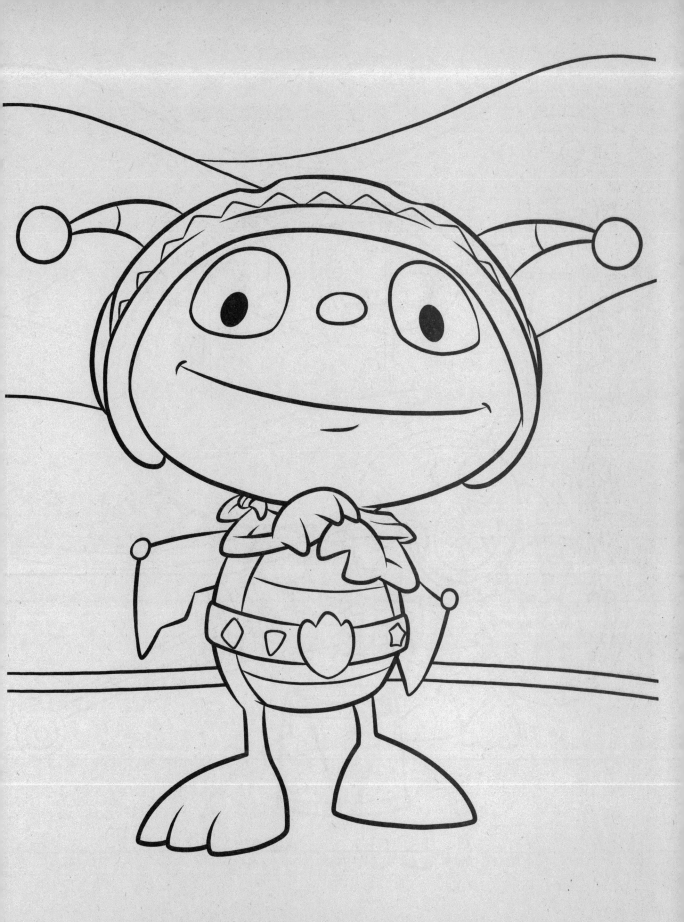

Henry knows Roberto really likes him.
That's why he copied him!

©Disney

Henry has a great idea. He's going to add green
stripes to his racer.

"I'm going to make my stripes orange," says Roberto.

Help Henry and Roberto get back to the Monster Scouts.

Answer:

Use the clues to figure out who will win the race.

1. The winner's racer has 2 big

2. The winner's racer has 2 tiny

3. The winner's racer does not have a

4. The winner has a star on his

"And the winner is . . . **Henry Hugglemonster!**"
Daddo announces.

All the racers earned a reward.
"My racing patch!" cheers Henry.

Which picture of Henry is different?

A

B

C

D

Answer: B

Henry is feeling like a super-monster.
He's ready to blast off to the moon.

©Disney

Looks like Daddo's going to get there first!

The megabouncer boots are Cobby's
most huggle-riffic invention ever!

Who can Henry leap over with his megabouncers?
Connect the dots to find out.

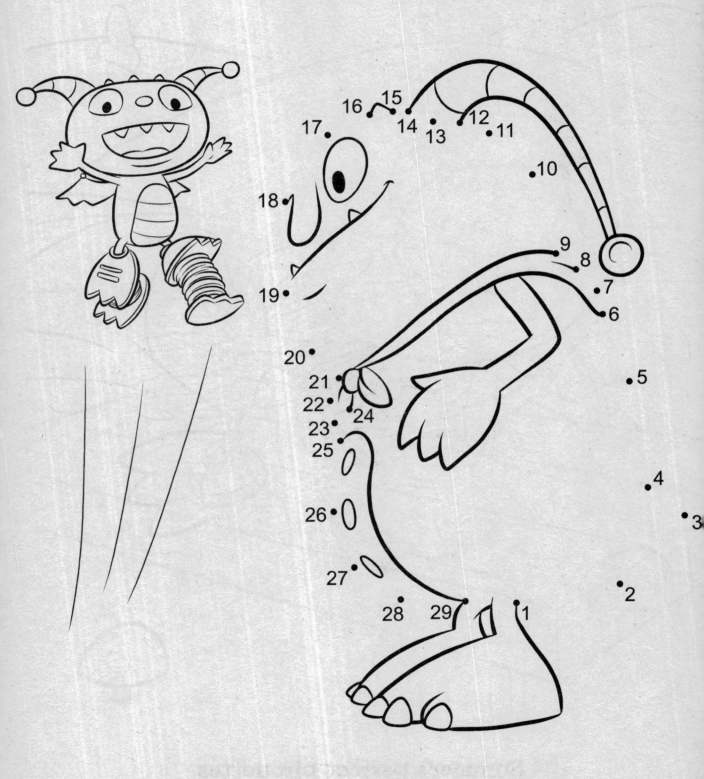

Summer's perfect pirouettes
have gotten a bit shaky.

©Disney

Denzel and Gertie love Henry's megabouncers!

Draw what Henry and his friends see up in the sky.

Denzel and Gertie can't wait to put
on their own megabouncers.

Henry's bouncing is getting in the way of
Summer's performance.

Henry, Denzel, and Gertie bounce
over a tree of Monsterbirds.

They spring over Grando in his hammock.

Circle the foods that begin with the letter S.

Answer:

It's time for Max and Ava's birthday party.
Oh, no, Henry!

©Disney

Bounce! Bounce! Bounce!

Look out, Mr. Growlerstein!

Help Summer find out who is ruining her perfect pirouettes.

End

Begin

"Do you know what this is all about?"
asks Signor Roartonio.

©Disney

Irving, Ava, and Max want to help
Summer, too!

10 cupcakes are hiding in the scene. Find and circle them!

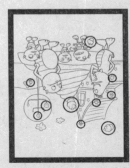

"What do we want?" shouts Summer.
"To find out who's shaking us!"
her friends shout back.

Officer Higgins stops Summer in her tracks.

©Disney

Then he gets bounced around, too!

Connect the dots to complete the picture.

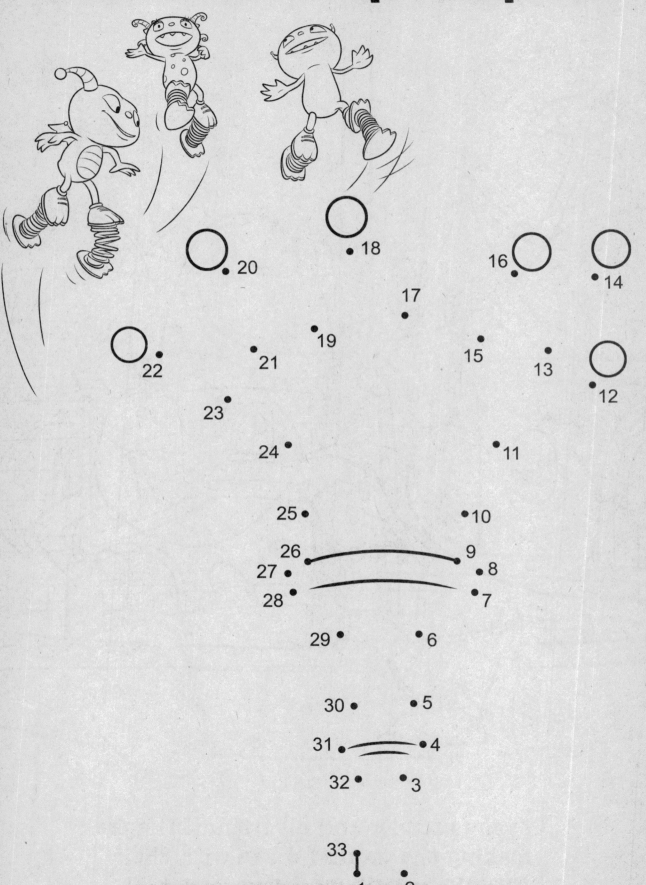

"It's my brother and his friends! They're making the ground shake with their **megabouncers**," says Summer.

"What are megabouncers?" wonders Max.

Henry bounces in to show Max his
totally roarsome boots.

"All your bouncing is causing the biggest mess ever!" says Summer.

Match the friends to the correct picture.

1

A

2

B

3

C

4

D

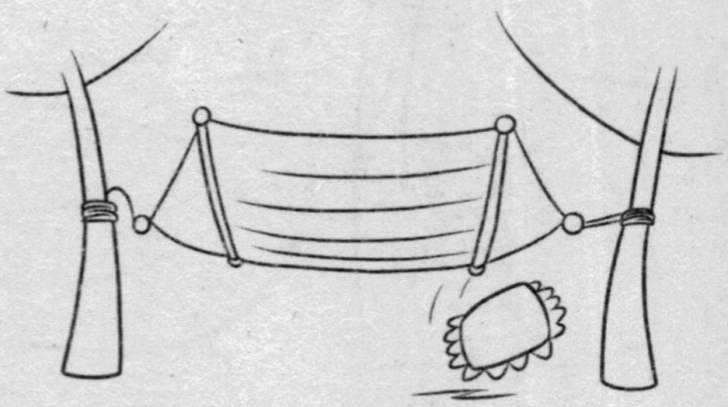

5

E

Answer: 1−D, 2−E, 3−B, 4−C, 5−A

"I feel really bad," says Gertie.

"Don't worry, Gertie," Henry says. "Hugglemonsters always find a way to make things better!"

Henry, Gertie, and Denzel clean up all
the messes.

Where can Henry and his friends bounce without bothering anyone?
Put a check next to the perfect bouncing spot.

Answer: